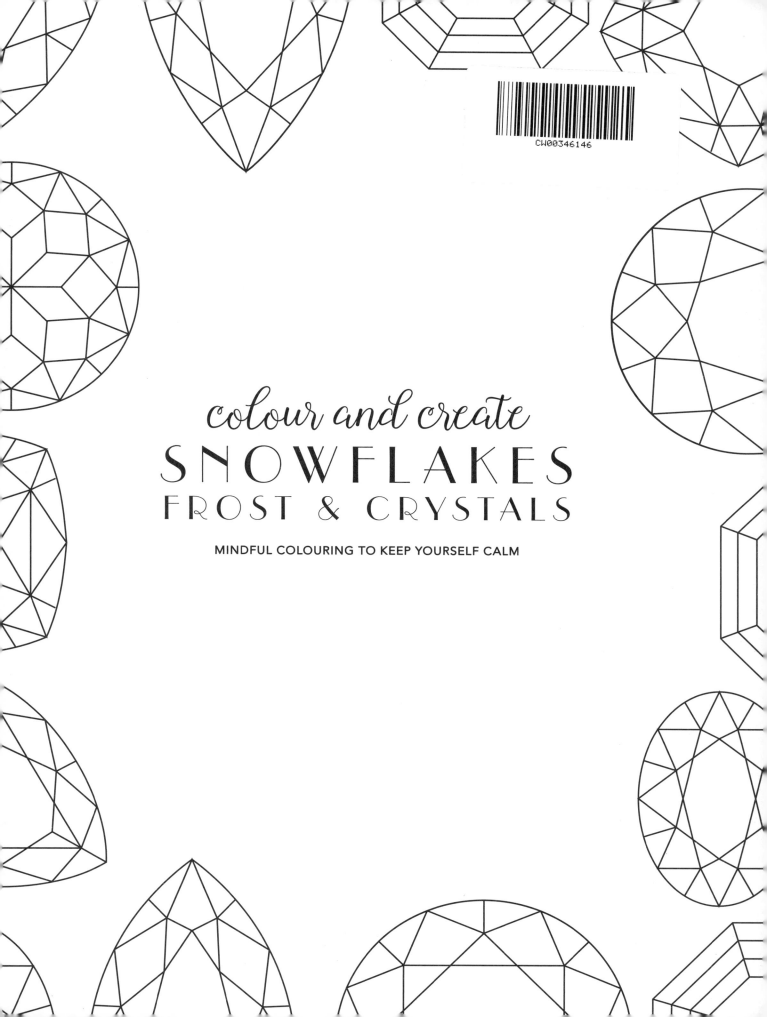

colour and create

SNOWFLAKES
FROST & CRYSTALS

MINDFUL COLOURING TO KEEP YOURSELF CALM

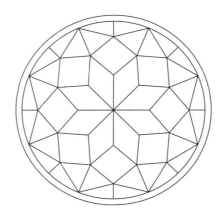

An Hachette UK Company
www.hachette.co.uk

First published in 2015 by Bounty Books, a division of Octopus Publishing Group Ltd
a division of Octopus Publishing Group Ltd
Carmelite House
50 Victoria Embankment
London, EC4Y 0DZ
www.octopusbooks.co.uk

ISBN: 978-0-75373-010-2

A CIP catalogue record for this book is available from the British Library

Printed and bound in China

10 9 8 7 6 5 4 3 2 1

Design Wide Open Studio
Text Shelia Hawkins
Publisher Samantha Warrington
Art Director Miranda Snow
Managing Editor Karen Rigden
Editor Phoebe Morgan
Production controller Katherine Hockley

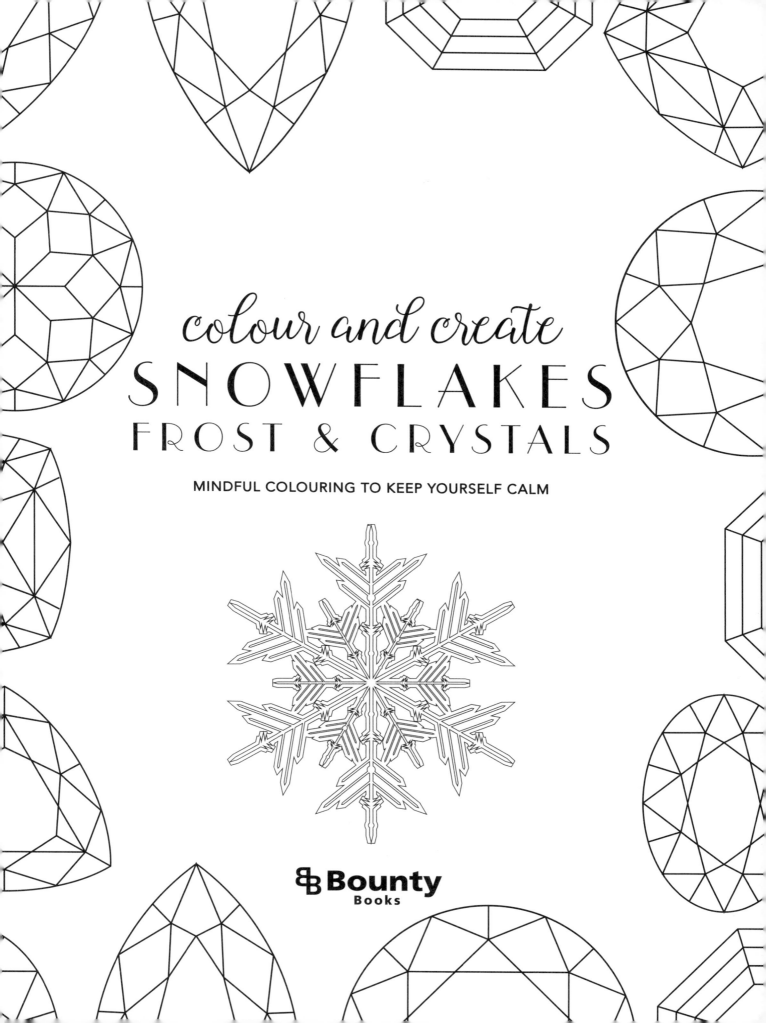

colour and create
SNOWFLAKES
FROST & CRYSTALS

MINDFUL COLOURING TO KEEP YOURSELF CALM

Bounty
Books

We are like a snowflake, all different in
our own beautiful way

Unknown

When snow falls, nature listens

Antoinette van Kleeff

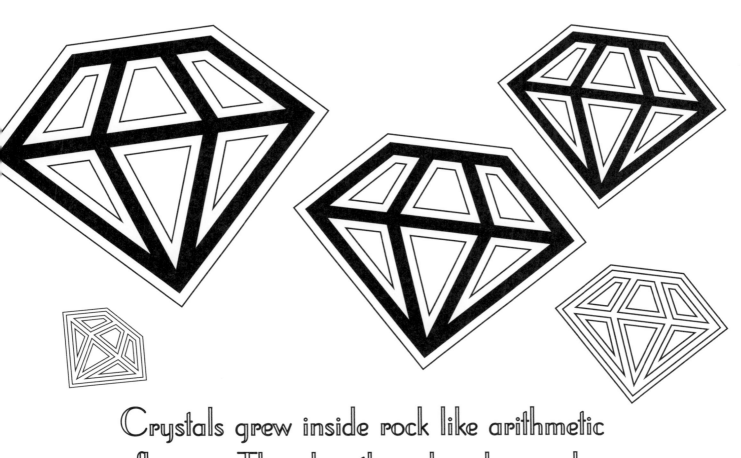

Crystals grew inside rock like arithmetic
flowers. They lengthened and spread,
added plane to plane in an awed and
perfect obedience to an absolute geometry
that even stones — maybe only the stones
— understood.

Annie Dillard

Snowflakes are one of nature's most fragile things, but just look what they can do when they stick together

Vista M Kelly

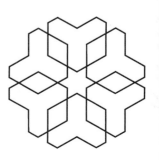

Silently, like thoughts come and go,
the snowflakes fall, each one a gem
William Gibson

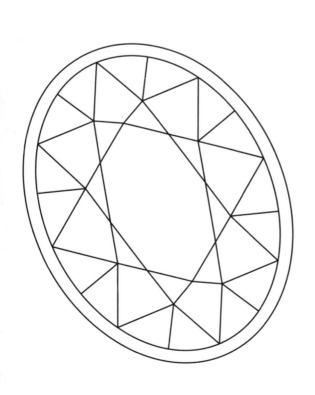

When there's snow on the ground
I like to pretend I'm walking on clouds

Takayuki Ikkaku

The first fall of snow is not only an event, it is a magical event. You go to bed in one kind of world and wake up in another quite different, and if this is not enchantment then where is it to be found?

J B Priestley

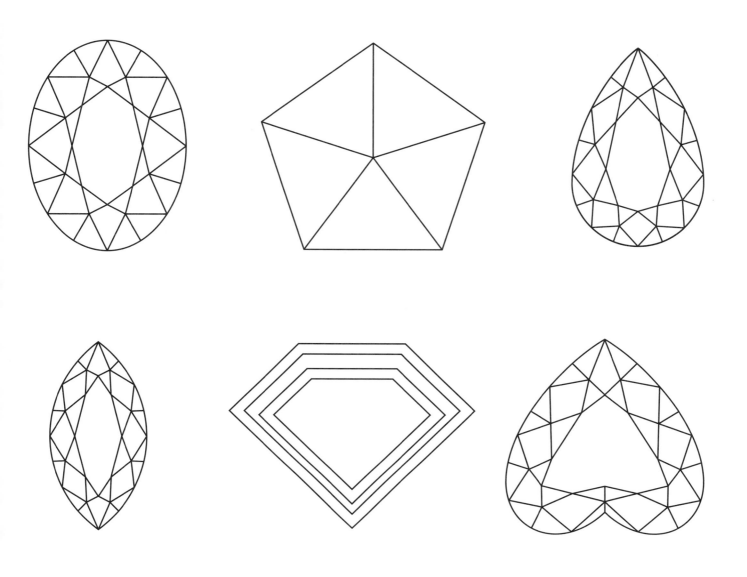

Life can't sparkle unless you do

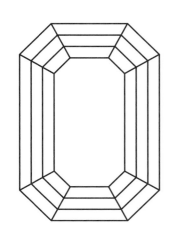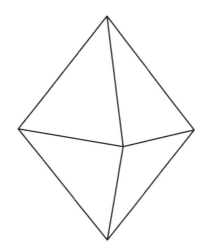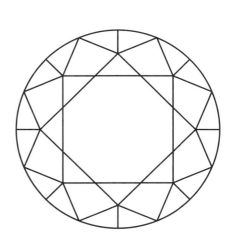

Snow is the endless repetition of an ordinary miracle

Orhan Pamuk

Snowflakes are kisses from heaven

Unknown

Every season has its melody.
It's up to us to find the rhythm and
bring it to life.

When in doubt, just add glitter

The sound of the blades on the ice in the
morning is like smelling fresh coffee

Tara Lipinski (Former American Ice Figure Skater)

Are ye the ghosts of fallen leaves,
O flakes of snow,
For which, through naked trees,
the winds A-mourning go?

John B. Tabb

You are unrepeatable.
There is a magic about you that
is all your own.

Snowmen fall from heaven... unassembled

Unknown

Never lose your sense of wonder

Let us love winter, for it is the spring of genius

Pietro Aretino

Like fragile ice, anger passes away in time

Ovid

Sparkle, shine, glitter and glow

You can't get too much winter
in the winter

Robert Frost

We build statues out of snow, and
weep to see them melt.

Walter Scott

I leaned out one last time and caught a snowflake on my tongue. It tasted so good, so pure and so divine, like nothing I had ever tasted from the sky.

Shannon A Thompson

A million feathers falling down,
A million stars that touch the ground,
So many secrets to be found
Amid the falling snow

When it snows you have two choices:
shovel or make snow angels
Unknown

Kindness is like snow — it beautifies everything it covers

Kahlil Gibran

The snow is sparkling like a million little suns

Lama Willa Mille

We have only this moment, sparkling like a star in our hand — and melting like a snowflake

Marie B Ray

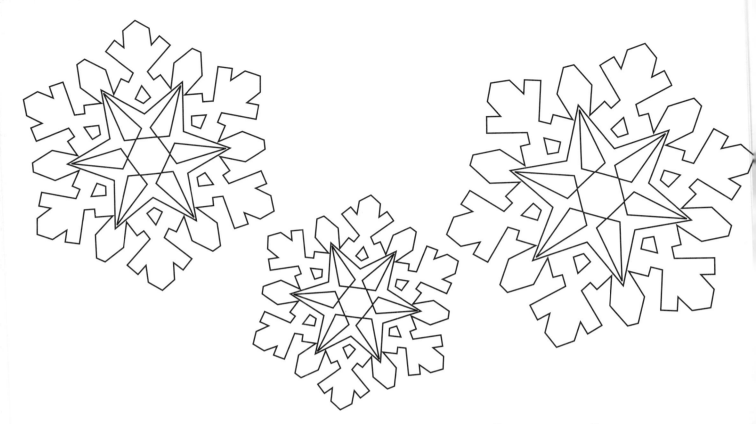

Snow provokes responses that reach
right back to childhood

Andy Goldsworthy

If we had no winter the spring
would not be so pleasant

Anne Bradstreet

One kind word can warm three winter months

Japanese proverb

Once, in the midst of a seemingly
endless winter, I discovered within myself
an invincible spring.

The future lies before you like a field of fallen snow;
Be careful how you tread it, for every step will show

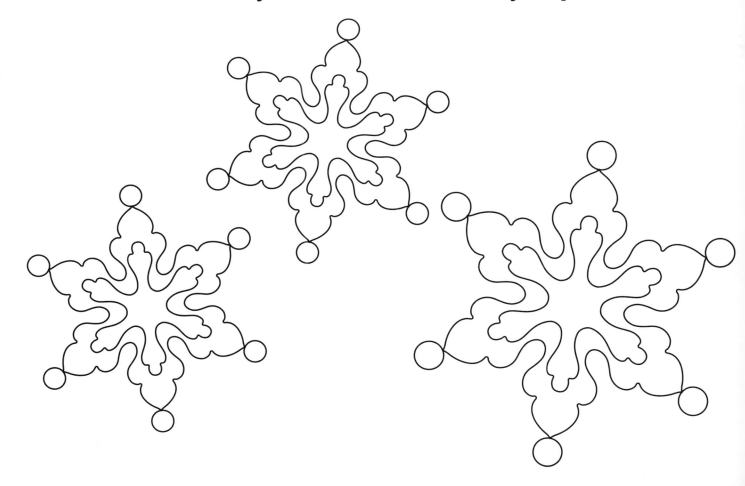

Snowflakes are winter's butterflies

Let it snow, let it snow, let it snow

Advice is like snow — the softer it falls, the longer it dwells upon, and the deeper it sinks into the mind.

Samuel Taylor Coleridge

I love snow, snow and all the forms of radiant frost

Percy Bysshe Shelley

I wasn't made for winter, I want my flip flops!

Baby it's cold outside!

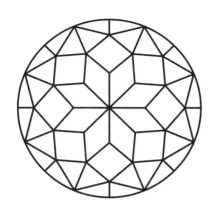 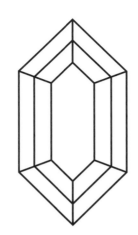 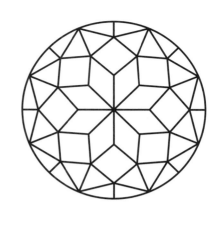

In a crystal we have a clear evidence of
the existence of a formative life principle, and although
we cannot understand the life of a crystal, it is
nonetheless a living being.

Nikola Tesla

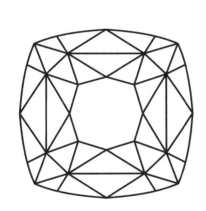 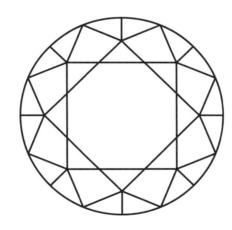 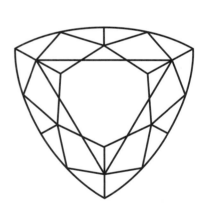

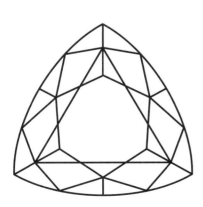  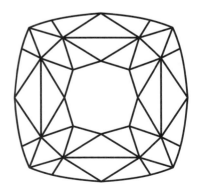

Don't let anyone dim your sparkle

Live, love, sparkle

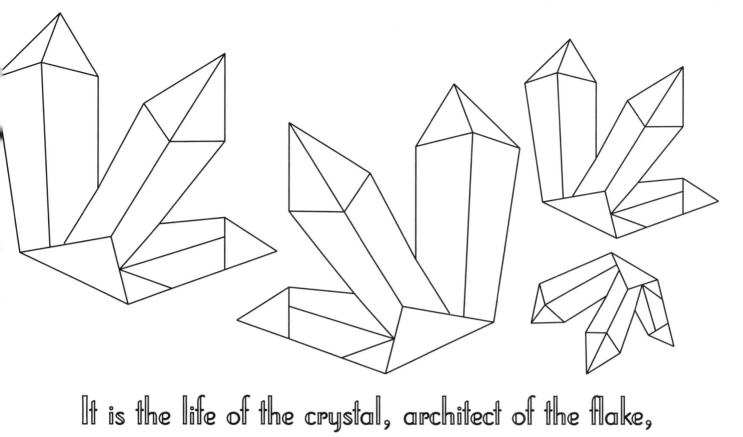

It is the life of the crystal, architect of the flake,
the fire of the frost, the soul of the sunbeam.
This crisp winter air is full of it.

John Burrows, "Winter Sunshine"

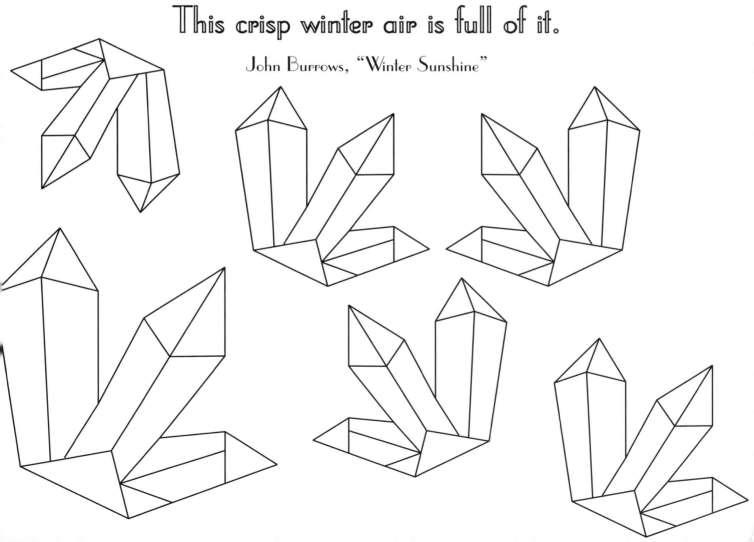

Let your inner sparkle shine through

You don't have to be rich to sparkle

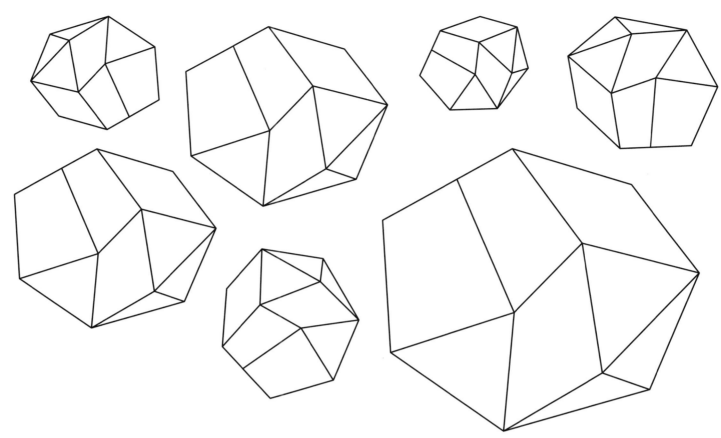

Leave a little sparkle wherever you go

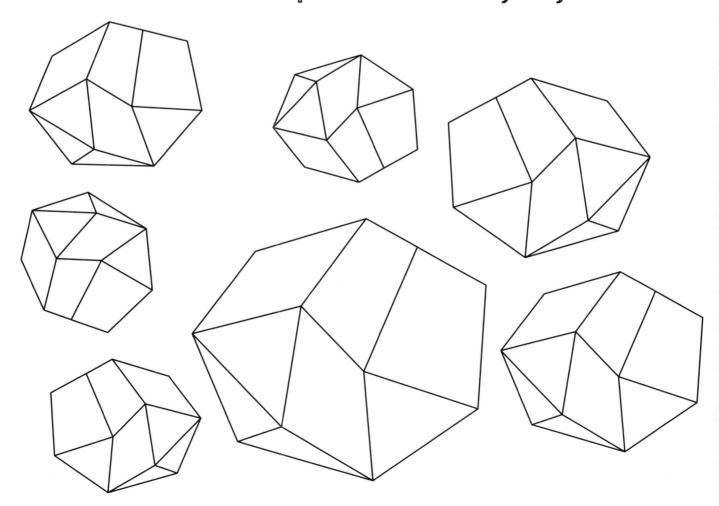

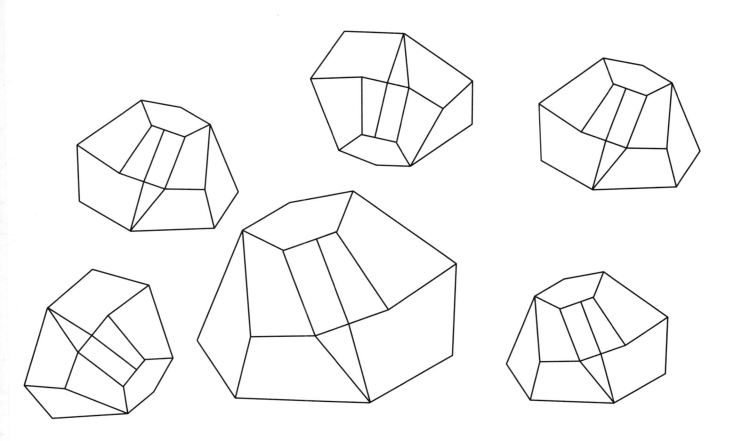

Crystals amplify the consciousness

Shirley Maclaine

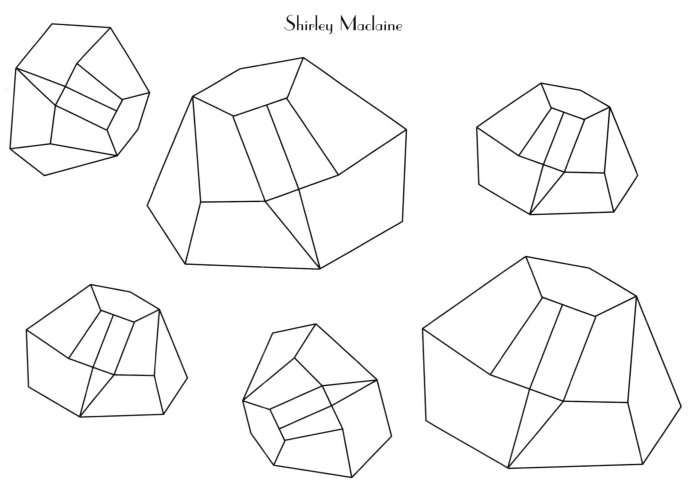

There's one good thing about snow, it makes your lawn
look as good as your neighbour's

Clyde Moore

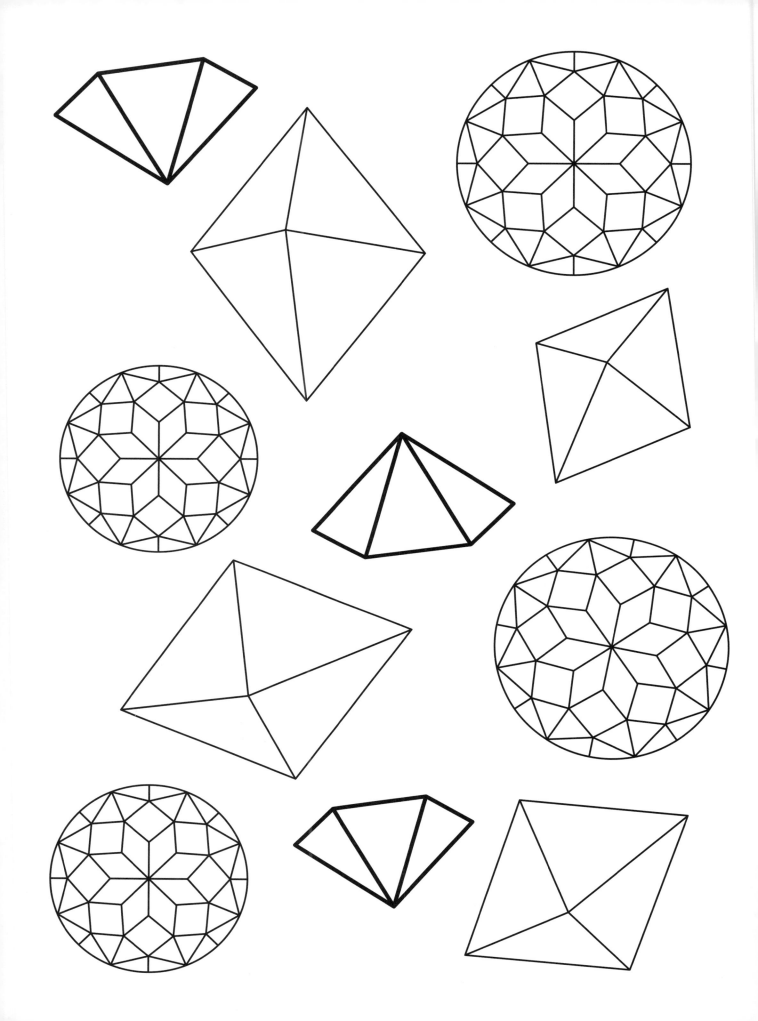

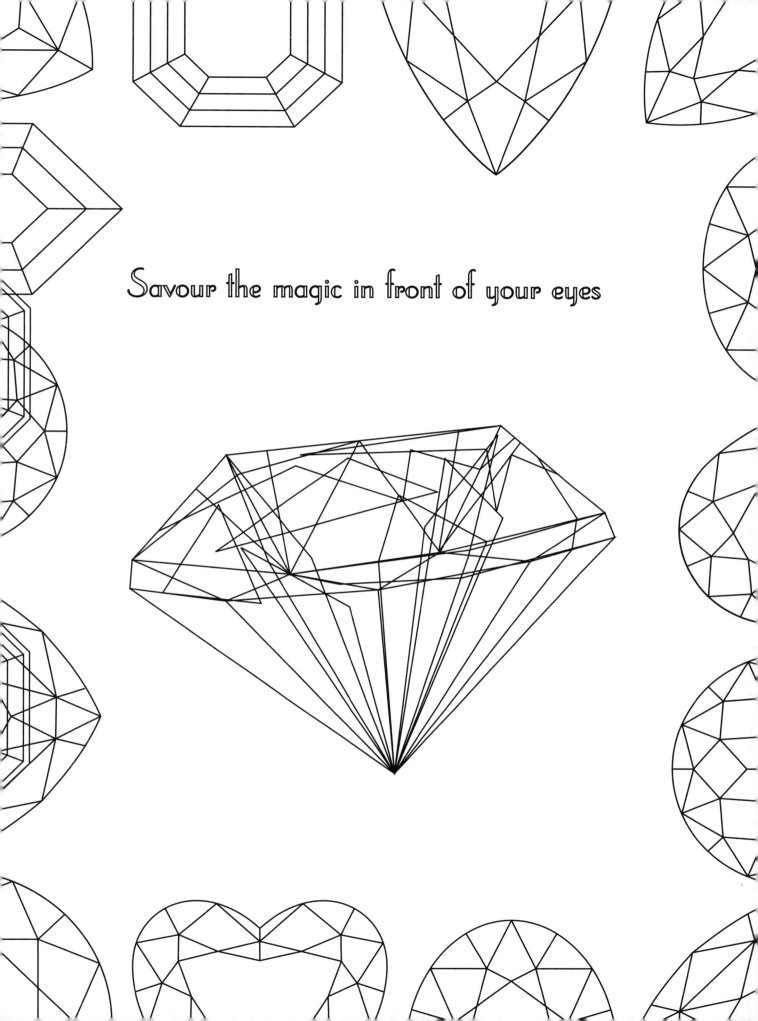

Savour the magic in front of your eyes

Loved ones, like precious gems,
bring colour to your life

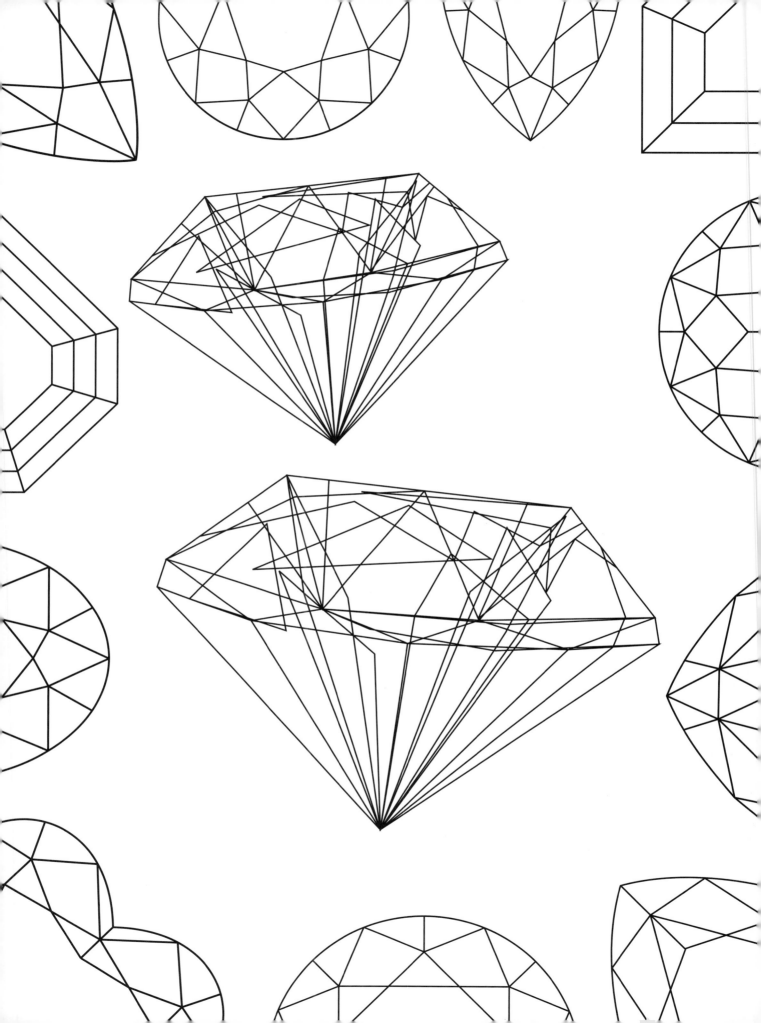

When we pay attention to nature's music, we find that everything on earth contributes to its harmony

Hazrat Inayat Khan